BRITAIN IN PICTURES
THE BRITISH PEOPLE IN PICTURES

BRITISH
WINDMILLS AND WATERMILLS

GENERAL EDITOR
W. J. TURNER

The Editor is most grateful to all those who have
so kindly helped in the selection of illustrations
especially to officials of the various public
Museums Libraries and Galleries and
to all others who have generously
allowed pictures and MSS
to be reproduced

BRITISH WINDMILLS AND WATERMILLS

C. P. SKILTON

WITH
8 PLATES IN COLOUR
AND
24 ILLUSTRATIONS IN
BLACK & WHITE

COLLINS · 14 ST. JAMES'S PLACE · LONDON
MCMXLVII

PRODUCED BY
ADPRINT LIMITED LONDON

PRINTED IN GREAT BRITAIN BY
CLARKE & SHERWELL LTD NORTHAMPTON
ON MELLOTEX BOOK PAPER MADE BY
TULLIS RUSSELL & CO LTD MARKINCH SCOTLAND

LIST OF ILLUSTRATIONS

PLATES IN COLOUR

BLACK AND WHITE ILLUSTRATIONS

THE RISE AND DECLINE OF WINDMILLS

THE millers and millwrights of England have almost disappeared into the books of social history. Their trades, through seven centuries, brought the staff of life to man, but now the mills stand derelict, creaking in the wind which once turned the great sails, or else eking out a precarious existence in a world of more modern production methods.

The late E. V. Lucas, in comparing the vanishing blacksmith and the vanishing miller, wrote that "With blacksmiths we can be on terms of intimacy; millers are distant and aloof. Blacksmiths are at our doors; millers mean a climb. Blacksmiths can be induced to turn aside from their normal work to make a boy's hoop; millers would never grind a special doll's bag of corn, not even for the Squire's only daughter. The shyest child can have a front seat at the smithy matinées, but it requires influence or rare gifts of persuasion and charm to be invited up the steps of a mill into the terrifying abode of thunder and whiteness."

Whatever may be thought about millers, a subject on which Chaucer, too, had something to say, their workplaces are a delight to the eye and, not surprisingly, have aroused the interest and enthusiasm of famous men. Robert Louis Stevenson said : "There are, indeed, few merrier spectacles than that of many windmills bickering together in a fresh breeze over a woody country ; their halting alacrity of movement, their pleasant business, making bread all day long with uncouth gesticulations, their air, gigantically human, as of a creature half alive, put a spirit of romance into the tamest landscape." Hilaire Belloc and Robert Bridges both wrote poems about windmills, and the same inspiration has provided the subjects of paintings by leading English artists.

There are doubtless several related reasons why the sight of a windmill should be a thrilling experience to anyone with an instinct for beauty. The principal reason, however, I believe to be this : like the nameless but revered masons of Gothic cathedrals, the builders of windmills can be believed to have poured their souls into their work, as indeed every craftsman does, but their creations are probably unparalleled as examples of working functional buildings.

A few windmills stand at the present day looking very much like those of Chaucer's time, their shape deriving from the purpose of the structure. Developments in later centuries led to the building of mills which do not bear a great resemblance to the early post-mills, but they too have the same perfect fitness of design, and the same careful workmanship in construction.

When the amount of labour that had to be put into the making of a windmill is considered, and the fact that almost no two windmills are architecturally identical is remembered, the achievements of the millwrights must be counted to be as astonishing and powerful in their way as Gothic and baroque church buildings seem to those who gaze upon them in our century. These men were the forerunners of the engineers of to-day, and indeed their scope was more than merely work upon mills, for the term "millwright," as meaning mechanical engineer, was in everyday use until the early nineteenth century.

It is in detail, perfectly assembled and delightfully situated, that we can find the greatest visual pleasure. Windmills can, as much as anything, show us "beauty on a high hill."

The earliest windmills in the British Isles have not been traced back beyond 1191, although the first known windmill had a very short life. Without the knowledge of Abbot Samson, who owned a watermill, Dean Herbert set up on his glebe lands at Haberdon a windmill, which greatly angered the Abbot, who, in spite of the Dean's protestations that the windmill was for his personal use only, brooked no competition, and ordered the destruction of the offending mill. Carlyle re-tells the story amusingly in *Past and Present*.

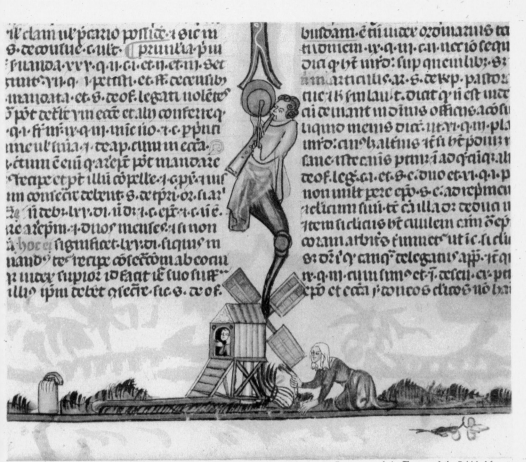

POST MILL IN THE 14TH CENTURY

Detail from a Decretal of Gregory IX

14th century MS written in Italy, illuminated in England

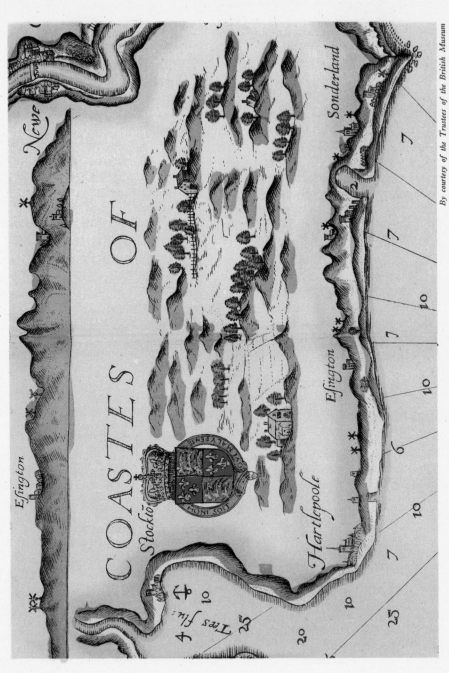

CHART SHOWING WINDMILLS AS LANDMARKS ON THE NORTH-EAST COAST OF ENGLAND

Detail from a coloured engraving in Waghenaer's *The Mariners' Mirrour*, 1588

William Morris, at the time of his death, possessed the Psalter which contains the earliest extant picture of a windmill. The date of the Psalter is believed to be about 1270, and the illustration shows a post-mill with four sails. Another thirteenth-century manuscript, in the British Museum, is Aristotle's *Physica* depicting a miller pushing his windmill round with the aid of the tail-pole. The Luttrell Psalter, made about seventy years after the one which Morris owned, shows the miller loading a sack of corn on to the shoulders of a customer, while a dog sits upon the tail-pole. Early portrayals of windmills also include a carved pew-end in Thornham Church, Norfolk, and a complicated misericord in Bristol Cathedral. Others which may be mentioned are a Flemish brass of 1349 in St. Margaret's Church, King's Lynn, and early stained-glass windows at Great Greenford, Middlesex, and Fairfield, Worcestershire. Much later connections between windmills and churches are recorded on tombstones in Friskney churchyard, Lincolnshire, although the wooden mill itself has now disappeared.

Andrew Myllar, Scotland's first printer, had as a colophon a windmill, which appeared in a book he had printed in 1506 at Rouen. Very probably this device was, however, cut by a French artist.

About this time, drinking-cups of curious construction were in vogue, one style being a windmill cup. An example is known dated 1619, made of silver, parcel-gilt, and 9½ inches high. At the top is a model gabled windmill, with a step-ladder behind, up which the miller is carrying a sack. There are also a dial and a tube attached to the mill. As the cup is bell-shaped, it can only be set down when empty, and to be filled must be inverted. After this operation the drinker would blow down the tube, setting the sails rotating and indicating the power of his lungs. Used as wager cups, the feat would be to fill the cup and drink the contents, before the sails, previously set in motion, had stopped revolving.

By the seventeenth century the windmill had long been an established feature of the English landscape ; with the watermill it was the only means of providing bread for the rural economy of mediæval times and later. Grinding merrily still in the nineteenth century, they were thus found by William Cobbett at Ipswich : "The windmills on the hills in the vicinage are so numerous that I counted, whilst standing in one place, no less than seventeen. They are all painted of washed white ; the sails are black ; it was a fine morning, the wind was brisk, and their twirling together added greatly to the beauty of the scene, which, having the broad and beautiful arm of the sea on one hand, and the fields and meadows, studded with farm houses, on the other, appeared to me the most beautiful sight of the kind I had ever beheld."

The so-called march of progress, however, was before long to alter the life of the countryside, of which the local mill was an integral part in Cobbett's day. The dusty miller, individualist, hard worker, experienced at his trade, clever engineer when occasion demanded, courageous when battling with storm, had to face the fact that new inventions and circumstances spelled extinction for him. Craftsmanship was everywhere to give way to mechanisation, but it was the introduction of the roller mills and the enormously improved transport facilities that were to end, for all practical purposes, the reign of the windmill. First here and then there windmills would stop, when competition from the giant modern mills no longer left enough work for them. Life had gone from their bodies and, unwanted relics of a vanishing era, they would decay and often be finally destroyed and forgotten. Others carried on, gathering some strength, perhaps, from the falling of their brethren, and work even until to-day. It cannot be conjectured when the last windmill will cease grinding ; to-day's owners were born in a time when working windmills were a commonplace, but at the end of the twentieth century a windmill still in production will certainly be an anomaly. "Behold ! a giant am I !" wrote Longfellow in a poem of the windmill in its days of power. The giant has fallen.

Families sometimes owned a windmill through several generations ; Uphill Mill, near Folkestone, was in the possession of the Kettle family, for instance, from 1790 to 1931, the entire period of its existence. Joseph Rank, the most famous miller of our time, was the son and grandson of windmill owners, and was born in a cottage attached to a tower-mill at Hull in 1854 ; from the upper floors of the latter more than a score of mills could be seen. When twenty-one years of age, he started in business on his own account, renting a small windmill in the same district, and doing all the work himself, including canvassing and delivery, and even dressing the millstones. In a biography of Rank, *Through the Mill*, by R. G. Burnett, are some revealing facts concerning windmill economics. In his first five years in business at Waddingham's Mill, Rank said he was grinding only twenty-five to thirty sacks of flour weekly, and selling two or three tons of provender. After doing his best he could clear only £5 a week, and found, in fact, that he had lost £200 over the whole period, even after the rather daring installation of an auxiliary gas engine. Accordingly, in 1880, he moved, and shared a larger windmill, which had flour-grinding and seed-crushing plant, with five pairs of French stones and one pair of grey stones. This mill he worked three days a week and rapidly recovered his losses and improved his financial position. In 1883 he saw a steel roller mill for the first time, at Tadcaster, and realising the enormous potential production capacity in comparison with the centuries-old methods, he built a similar mill at Hull two years later with an output of six sacks an hour, and by the turn of the century was the foremost miller in Britain.

Rank's early expansions were made at a time when there was great depression in the milling industry, a report upon which was issued by a special committee of the National Association of British and Irish Millers in 1887. It mentioned that although the population of England and Wales

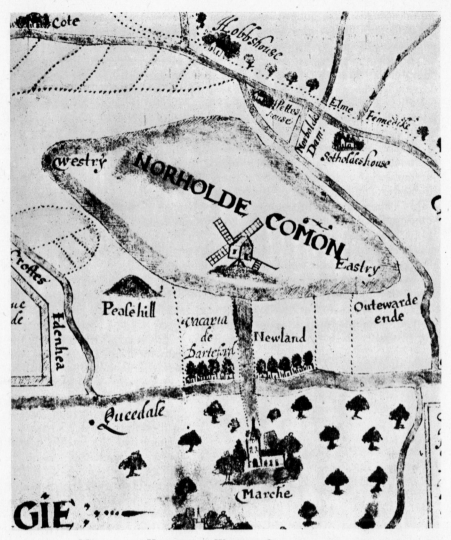

MAP OF THE HUNDRED OF WISBECH, CAMBRIDGESHIRE, 1597
Detail from a copy made in 1657

had increased from approximately eighteen millions to twenty-six millions between 1851 and 1881, the number of men engaged in milling had fallen from 36,076 to 23,462 over the same period. Cheap American flour was flooding Britain, backed by the vast wheatlands of the United States and extensive roller mills operating there. Old-fashioned milling in Britain

11

would actually have gone into a decline, faced with this competition, even if no roller mills had ever been built in this country, but now, with greatly increased general output, and good transport facilities, no longer was a locality dependent upon the nearby windmill; bread could just as easily be obtained through the new sources. Each roller mill had the capacity of dozens, perhaps hundreds of the windmills it superseded, and it has been noted that a score of the new flour mills between Gravesend and Isleworth can provide the material for making 2,250,000,000 pounds of bread each year.

Towns were spreading, too, and fields and copses disappearing under the onslaught of building development. Sometimes, windmills would be surrounded by these suburbs: there were examples, for instance, at Rochester (pulled down in 1946) and at Sunderland. Biscot Mill, near Luton, was standing in open country, a beautiful specimen of a working smock mill, in the early part of this century, and after it ceased activity about 1920, and was shorn of its sails, it still remained a landmark amid the cornfields. By 1938, however, it was surrounded by houses and roads, allowed to decay, and was finally demolished.

Nowadays, a number of trades which were essential and thriving a century ago, are dying or dead. Blacksmiths, wheelwrights, harness-makers, thatchers, millers and millwrights of the old school are well on the way out. No young man is likely to apprentice himself to a trade without prospects, and probably millwrighting as such is the most nearly extinct of all the trades mentioned. It follows that even where windmills are still at work, it will be difficult and costly to repair them in the event of breakdown or accident, and at the present time such a happening may seal the fate of a mill otherwise structurally sound.

Then, too, the work of a miller is more than usually hard, and likely to be unattractive to men with a modern outlook. The wind must be caught while it blows, which may mean long and irregular hours, and working sometimes on Sunday or at night time. Many windmills now have auxiliary engine-power installed, so that they are not so much at the mercy of the fickle wind.

SOUTH-WEST PROSPECT OF YORK
Detail of an engraving by B. Cole, 1731

MILLWRIGHTS' TRADE CARD
Eighteenth century engraving

13

Although, fortunately, workmanship of an extremely high order went into the building of windmills, they remain susceptible to two deadly attacks : fire, and the fury of wind and storm. These have accounted for the end of many mills ; sails get torn off, a post-mill may even be overturned, or the whole thing go up in a great pyrotechnic display. Fires were often caused through the effects of storm upon the mechanism of the mill, and friction induced by the efforts of the miller to control it. The breeze which is necessary, unless auxiliary power is available, for the working of the windmill, can, if it becomes over-powerful, develop from a friend into a cruel foe.

At the present time, there are two thousand derelict windmills in Britain, but less than a hundred working. The Society for the Protection of Ancient Buildings, founded by William Morris in 1877, has a special windmill and watermill section, which is constantly engaged in watchful protection and preservation. It is possible, too, for a local authority to make an Order under the Town and Country Planning Act of 1932, for the purpose of preserving windmills, and the Essex County Council was the first to move under this Act, scheduling a number of mills in 1938.

The windmills which are still in working order are mostly used for the grinding of animal foods or else are draining mills. In the course of their existence mills have been put to use for grinding of all kinds and for timber-sawing and other purposes.

The miller and his mill have fallen on bad times, and their vicissitudes are many. The career, while not typical, of a charming whitewashed windmill which many thousands of holidaymakers to Blackpool must have seen on the sea front at Lytham St. Anne's can, with its predecessors, serve to epitomise the whole history of windmills. Chronicles of Lytham mention a mill as far back as the twelfth century, and in a deed of 1327 the Prior speaks of the 'wyn milne.' The present structure, a tower-mill with walls several feet thick at the base, was built in 1762, and incorporated a piece of leadwork dated 1663. In 1919 the mill was gutted by a fire started during a gale, although up to that time it was in production. The local corporation restored it to a pleasant semblance of its former outward appearance, and it became a cafe and then the headquarters of a motor-boat club. Finally it was taken over by the electricity department and used as a transformer station.

Not every windmill has the same potentialities for conversion to a useful purpose as this Lancashire example, but it is likely that of the three main types of windmill, the brick tower-mills have the best possibilities for survival. The ideal to be aimed at is to keep as many windmills working as possible, but where there is no longer any hope of this there is no reason why the structure should not have another lease of life by being put to other uses, for it will be a sad day for the English landscape when no more of these beautiful edifices exist.

MILL ON THE BURE
Chalk drawing by John Sell Cotman, 1841

WINDMILL DESIGN AND MECHANISM

THE earliest type of windmill, and therefore the kind which appears in ancient representations, is known as the post-mill, and is so named from the fact that the structure pivots on a central post.

A typical post-mill rests on four piers of brick or stone upon which are laid two beams at right-angles to each other, known as cross-trees, and often a foot square. The post, the central pivot, rises from the intersection of the cross-trees, and is supported by strong quarter-bars, which are inclined trestle-wise between the horizontal cross-trees and the vertical post. In later centuries this portion was sometimes enclosed by a round brick or wooden wall, roofed over, and known as a roundhouse. This protected the wooden beams, and also provided a store for the miller, most roundhouses having either just the ground floor or one extra floor.

Above all this rises the working superstructure, which will be weather-boarded, and of a box-like shape, curving to an arch at the top. Across the body of the mill, from side to side, is a beam up to two feet square, called the crown-tree, resting on the post previously described. There are usually three floors in the superstructure, arranged according to the following plan.

On the top floor are bins into which the grain is poured, descending to the stones on the floor below through an agitated trough, or shoe, by an arrangement which ensures that the amount of grain passing down is in direct ratio to the speed of the sails. The grain goes through a hole ("eye") in the centre of the upper stone, which rotates, while the lower stone of the pair, the bed stone, remains stationary. The stones are grooved according to a regular system on their facing surfaces, and it is the action of these grooves which grinds the grain. The upper stone can be raised and adjusted to allow for the various kinds of grain which may be ground, or the particular result required. It has been recorded that a pair of stones should be able to grip brown paper at the eye, newspaper in the middle, and tissue paper at the edge. Stones, incidentally, would average a little over four feet in width, and three-quarters of a ton in weight, originating from Derbyshire ("Peak" stones) or from France ("burr" stones). The grain is gradually worked out between the stones until it emerges as flour or meal from the outer edge and finally passes through a hole in the floor, by spouts to reception bins on the lowest storey, from which there is exit by means of an exterior ladder. The meal at this stage is quite hot, owing to the friction during grinding, and it is important that the miller should watch for any mishaps during working, or a fire may quickly result. For this reason a warning bell is rigged to ring when the grain in the hoppers on the upper floor has run out.

The sails are carried by the windshaft which inclines downward at a slight angle through the body of the mill in order to help support the considerable weight of the sails, which might otherwise cause the whole structure to overbalance. Immediately inside the body is a large cog-wheel known as the brake-wheel, and the sails can be stopped by a rim-brake upon this wheel. At the rear end of the windshaft, which is possibly a ton in weight, there may be another cog-wheel known as the tail-wheel. The latter often drives one pair of stones direct, but the brake-wheel drives its stones, sometimes several pairs, plus the sack-hoist, through other cogwheels.

Outside, at the front of the windshaft, is an iron casting through which are mortised the two long "stocks" upon which the four sails are mounted. The oldest type of sail consists of a wooden framework over which is stretched canvas, to sword-point, dagger-point, first reef or full sail. These "common" sails had to be adjusted by hand when the wind varied greatly, each sail being brought in turn to the bottom and furled or unfurled by the miller, necessitating climbing up and down each sail. When wind variations were frequent, it was obviously a great nuisance to the miller to have to keep stopping his windmill in order to reef the sail, especially in rainy weather.

About 1770 an improvement was made when Andrew Meikle, a Scot who is credited with having invented the threshing-machine, introduced

FORD ROAD AND ROPE WALK SHOWING THE WINDMILL, NEAR FOLKESTONE

Water colour by John Constable, 1833

RANDALL'S MILL, NINE ELMS
Water colour by John Varley, 1830

the spring-sail, something like a Venetian blind, whereby the shutters of which the sails were comprised would be forced open by a strong wind, thus lessening the wind-resistance and the speed of the mill. They would close again when at the lowest point of the sail's circular journey, being out of the wind. These sails, however, had also to be adjusted separately to some extent, as the tension of the spring had to be controlled by means of a sail-rod to which the shutters were connected. William Cubitt, afterwards a famous canal and railway engineer, introduced in 1807, when only twenty-two, the "self-reefing" or "patent" sail, which was almost fully automatic. By this method a hole was bored through the windshaft which carried the sails, and a striking-rod inserted, the rear end of which was connected with an outside wheel upon which a chain was suspended with weights on it. If the wind is blowing too strong for safety, at a certain point the shutters of the sail in the wind are forced open, and the sail-rods of the others are simultaneously engaged and the position of the shutters changed. The only work for the miller to do is to adjust the weights so that he can arrange for the shutters to be closed to any predetermined limit. The shuttered sails did not develop the same power as the old-type canvas-rigged ones, but owing to their obvious superiority in convenience almost entirely superseded the latter, except that a compromise was sometimes effected by the use of two common and two spring-sails. When wind-mills are disused the shutters are often dismantled and only a framework of sail left, in order to decrease wind-resistance.

Since it is necessary to bring the sails into the wind and keep them there, until two centuries ago post-mills had to be turned bodily by a tail-pole, the steps being lifted clear of the ground. Being built by craftsmen engineers, mills are usually so well balanced that it is possible to move them by means of the tail-pole and one hand, once the inertia has been overcome, but the same objection applies here as with common sails ; the miller may have to keep leaving his work in order to accommodate his mill to wind variations. In 1750, Andrew Meikle, to whom, incidentally, the great John Rennie was apprenticed as a millwright, invented the fan-tail mechanism which turns the sails into the wind automatically. The fan-tail consists of a set of small vanes arranged in the shape of a wheel and erected at the rear of the mill at right-angles to the sails proper. It comes into action whenever the wind changes to set it into operation, by turning the mill round until the wind catches the sails once again, when the fan-tail is becalmed. Owing to the extremely low gear ratio, about 3,000 to 1, it is possible for a small fan-tail to turn a mill of considerable size in this way. The most usual position for the fan-tail was on a wheeled carriage attached to the tail-pole ; occasionally this would run on a circular rail on the ground around the mill. Less often the fan-tail would be mounted at the top rear end of the mill superstructure itself, where it was probably in a better position to be caught by the wind.

HAVERHILL TOWER-MILL, SUFFOLK
Pencil drawing by A. van Anrooy, 1942

In the middle of the sixteenth century a great development took place in windmill design, and two other kinds of mill appeared, similar to each other in principle, but quite different from the post-mill. These are the smock-mill, usually octagonal, the body of which is built of wood, and the tower-mill, which has a brick body, normally round. In both of these types of mill only the top cap, with sails attached, is turned into the wind, the remainder being stationary. Originally the cap, which turns on a track, was moved by a long tail-pole or by pulling an endless chain round a wheel suitably geared to the cap. Later, of course, Meikle's fan-tail was generally installed. Both the smock-mill and tower-mill may often be seen with a stage around the body to facilitate attention to the sails, and another gallery around the cap. Naturally, the solid foundation and construction of these later types make them more able than the post-mill to resist decay.

Some of these windmills were of considerable size. A famous example of a white smock-mill, the Russell Union Mill, still

POST-MILL AT SPROWSTON, NORWICH
Pencil drawing by Stanley J. Wearing, 1932

19

working at Cranbrook, Kent, was built in 1814 at a reputed cost of £3,500. It stands seventy feet from the ground to the top of the cap, and has seven storeys, three of these being in the brick base. A model of this mill is in the Science Museum, London. Tower-mills have been known even higher than this, the largest working example still in existence being Sutton Mill, near Hickling in Norfolk.

While it is usual to think of a windmill as having four sails, examples are known with five, six, or even eight sails, the only one with this last number still existing being at Heckington, Lincolnshire, a century-old specimen working until recently and driving five pairs of stones and a saw. The disadvantage of a five-sailed mill is that it is impossible to work the mill with a lesser number of sails should one become damaged or destroyed during a gale. A six-sailed mill, however, can be operated with four, three, or two sails, and it is certainly not uncommon for a windmill to be kept going with only two sails, when it does not lose much power compared with a complement of four. Post-mills with more than four sails are definitely unusual, although a prominent example with six sails stood in Sussex near Lewes until it was blown down in 1916. A model of this mill, with others, may be seen in Worthing Museum. Another variant, of which only one example still exists, and that in a very bad condition, had an annular, or ring-shaped sail. The mill at Haverhill, Suffolk, of this type, was last worked in 1933, and was an eight-storeyed tower-mill with a circular sail fifty feet in diameter, constructed on eight stocks, and with 120 vanes five feet long and one foot wide. Unfortunately the condition of this mill deteriorated and the machinery was dismantled in 1942 for war purposes.

John Smeaton (to whom the Royal Society awarded its gold medal in 1759 for his paper on windmills and watermills), who is most famous for the building of the Eddystone Lighthouse, appears to have been the first to make scientific investigation into windmill sails. He discovered that sails were most effective when given a slight twist, the ideal "weather," or angle which the surface of the sail makes with its plane of revolution, decreasing from 18° at the windshaft to 7° at the extremity of the sail. Smeaton declared that windmills with common sails of thirty feet developed the power of ten men or two horses. This, however, seems an under-estimate, for a large mill with several pairs of stones can develop forty horse-power. An increase in the size or number of sails, however, by no means increases the power in proportion. Naturally the more powerful smock- and tower-mills could accommodate larger sails than the post-mills, and sails have been recorded over forty feet long and nine feet wide. Incidentally Smeaton built a tower-mill which still exists at Newcastle-upon-Tyne, although it is no longer working. It had a cast-iron windshaft, and five sails, the first ever built with this number.

It is worthy of note that mills varied in sail-speed, some revolving

TOWER-MILL, WALPOLE HIGHWAY, NEAR WISBECH
Water colour by Barbara Jones, 1942

21

WINDMILL AT THURNE, NORFOLK
Oil painting by Edward Seago, 1946

slowly compared with neighbours which went possibly twice as fast because of lower gearing. An average speed would be about one complete revolution of the sails to eight of the stones. Another curious fact about windmills is that with some the sails would revolve in a clockwise direction, with others it would be anti-clockwise. The right-handed mill (anti-clockwise viewed from the exterior) was much the more common, and would have sails, stones and brake-lever opposite to those in a left-handed mill.

The output of some mills was quite large. Hodson's Mill at Brighton, which existed from 1804 to 1866, and was a twelve-sided smock-mill carrying three pairs of stones could, it is said, grind twenty-five loads a week (equivalent to 1,000 bushels or 70,000 pounds.) Bozeat post-mill, Northamptonshire, built in 1761, could grind six bushels hourly with a steady wind and half as much again with a strong wind. The sails of this mill were twenty-five feet long,

THE WINDMILLS OF BRITAIN

THERE is little doubt that Holland is the country which first springs to mind when one thinks of windmills, and the Dutch have certainly made great use of them not only for grinding but for pumping and sawing as well, and their windmills all seem to be of particularly charming types. Windmills exist in other lands, too, varying vastly in conception and construction. In Portugal there are tubby ones with canvas-rigged jib sails ; in Bessarabia you may see several six-sailed specimens close together in a straight line. Frank Brangwyn painted them in Spain, Sweden, Belgium, France and Germany, and indeed from the Frisian Islands and Sark to St. Helena and Barbados (where they are worked on the sugar plantations) you can find windmills.

We in Britain, however, should be proud of our mills, which represent a vast variety of types, and are not less beautiful than those of any other country in the world. True, they have been decimated in the course of the last hundred years, but we can hope that that process has now largely been halted through energetic action on the part of those interested in preservation.

We have seen that formerly more than twenty windmills could be counted from one spot, now no such spectacular feast can delight our eyes. Two windmills together is commonly the most we can see, and several pairs do in fact exist, the most famous undoubtedly being "Jack and Jill," the Clayton Mills, which will be familiar on a ridge of the South Downs to any observant railway traveller from London to Brighton. Jack's working life was from 1866 to 1906 ; a tower-mill, he is now used as a house, and is sailless. Jill is a little white post-mill with the sails still in position, but now also out of commission. Another pair in the home counties, this time a smock-mill and a post-mill, are at Outwood. The smock-mill, a comparative newcomer, has been idle for years, but the post-mill is not only the sole working windmill in Surrey, but the oldest working windmill in the whole country, being built in 1665, and remaining much the same as then. It is remarkable that the original deeds of the mill still exist, and show Thomas Budgen to have been the first in a long line of millers there. Tradition has it that the Great Fire of London was seen from this mill.

Only slightly younger is the open-trestle post-mill at Brill, Buckinghamshire, built in 1668, but no longer working; there is another of great age at Bourn, Cambridgeshire, which stopped operations in the middle 'twenties. This mill is possibly older than the others, for it has the earliest straight-gabled roof pattern instead of the rounded type which became popular later, but no proof of its date of erection has been discovered. Certainly earlier than these, and having the distinction of being designed by the famous architect Inigo Jones, is a windmill at Chesterton, in Warwickshire. The building was erected in 1632 as an observatory, however, and is a round stone structure standing on six arches. Converted into a windmill much later in life, it is the most peculiar construction ever to have borne sails.

South-east England, East Anglia and the Fylde in Lancashire are three parts of the country that are particularly strong in windmill history. In other parts windmills were almost non-existent, and the watermill held sway. Sussex is a county of numerous windmills and a few watermills, but its neighbour, Hampshire, is almost devoid of the former. A few examples are known, but as any visitor to Hampshire will realise, the numerous streams make good opportunities for watermills. The same obtains further along the coast, Devonshire being thickly studded with watermills; Somerset possesses a few windmills, but many watermills also. In Cornwall, a tower-mill at Padstow has been converted into a water-tower.

Sussex and Kent along the south coast, then, are the windmill counties. Both have many interesting examples. The roundhouse of the post-mill at High Salvington, near Worthing, is used as a tea-room, and the machinery in the upper floors is intact and may be viewed. This windmill was the first to be insured against fire, in 1774, and bears the dated seal of the Sun Insurance Company. At Littlehampton, the commanding tower-mill which existed for over a century until it was pulled down in 1934 (to make room for the funfair which disfigures the foreshore of this resort) also contained timber of unusual interest, for the main shaft during the later half of the mill's career consisted of part of the mast of a famous racing yacht of the 'fifties, the Duke of Norfolk's *Arundel*.

According to Horsfield's history of Sussex, published in 1835, "few spots are more visited in the summer months than the Miller's Tomb, by the frequenters of the neighbouring watering-places; and the extensive, rich and varied panoramic views amply repay the trouble of a pilgrimage to the tomb of Miller Oliver." This may still be seen at High Down Hill, near Worthing, and is the resting place of an eccentric miller who owned a nearby smock-mill, and who prepared his tomb at the age of 57, although he did not die until the age of 84, in 1793.

It was also in Sussex, in 1797, that an extraordinary removal took place, when the West Mill, Brighton, was hauled to a spot near Preston village, a distance of about five miles, by a team of 86 yoke of oxen belonging to farmers of the locality. Another removal is recorded in 1848 when a mill was taken from Slough, Buckinghamshire, by barge along the Thames and the Medway to Luton, near Chatham in Kent. Both of these mills disappeared during the course of the last century.

A mill of some musical and literary interest once existed at Strood, when a barrel-organ with sixteen tunes, superseded at a church near Maidstone, was acquired by the Strood miller and installed so that the sails set the music going while the mill was at work. It is stated that Charles Dickens, who lived in the vicinity, would sometimes walk to the windmill and

listen to the barrel-organ playing. This mill was destroyed by fire soon after Dickens's death.

A trade token, made of copper, was issued by William Packham of the Union Mill at Appledore, Kent, in 1794, and showed a picture of the smock-mill on one side while on the other was the inscription "Peace Innocence and Plenty." The Union Mill was built by the capital of a group of local farmers. Another token of this part of England was John Hoad's Maidstone Windmill Inn token, 1657, showing an open-trestle post-mill.

One hundred and fifty years ago, London retained much of its rural look, but during the course of the nineteenth century most of these evidences of an earlier and less industrialised age were swept away. The population increased enormously—in 1801 it was only 864,845—and as time went on the size of London became larger and larger, until eventually some portions of the home counties were formally adopted as part of the County of London under the Local Government Act, 1888. Those who are familiar with central London will know many place-names—Millbank, Great Windmill Street and others—having milling connections, and in nearly every case we have some slight knowledge of the mill that existed in olden times. All over the country, indeed, it may be fairly confidently assumed that streets, lanes, cottages, named in similar fashion mark the sites of windmills and watermills which once stood nearby.

In the sixteenth century several mills existed at Finsbury, while Shakespeare records another in *Henry IV*, Part 2, Act III, Scene ii. *Shallow*: "O, Sir John, do you remember since we lay all night in the windmill in St. George's fields?" *Falstaff*: "No more of that, good Master Shallow, no more of that." *Shallow*: "Ha, it was a merry night." This mill, standing on the south side of the Thames, survived for many years after Shakespeare wrote about it, and being at that time situated in the environs of the city, was suitably placed for such dissipation.

Various other mills existed through the centuries at Lambeth; pictures may be found showing mills which, unless quite inaccurately drawn, must be of different examples. One picture, about 1750, shows two post-mills with roundhouses near the river; an etching by Thomas Nugent, about 1770, while appearing to be far from faithful, illustrates the same in relation to the shot-tower which still stands and is in operation at the south side of Waterloo Bridge. Another drawing is of a smock-mill, with fan-tail and gallery, elevated on a brick base. All these mills disappeared years ago, as have one at Vauxhall, depicted in a lithograph of 1829, Randall's Mill at Nine Elms, a sturdy tower-mill standing on the water's edge, and others at Battersea, where stood a post-mill and later smock-mills near the Red House, a famous sporting and entertainment ground which was also the winning-post of many boat-races.

Battersea, also, was the home of a most curious mill, Captain Stephen Hooper's "horizontal air mill," built in 1801 for grinding linseed, and later converted to a

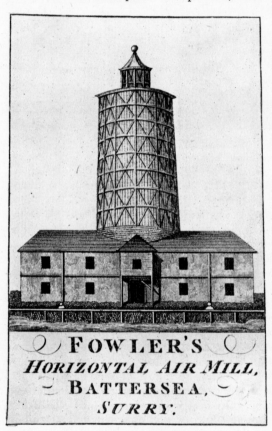

FOWLER'S HORIZONTAL AIR MILL, BATTERSEA
Nineteenth century engraving

HOLLOW POST-MILL, WIMBLEDON COMMON
Engraving by George Cooke, 1781-1834

malt mill. Its height, from the foundation, was 140 feet, and Hughson, in his *Circuit of London*, informs us that "the outer part consists of ninety-six shutters, eight feet high and nine inches broad, which, by the pulling of a rope, open and shut in the manner of a Venetian blind. Inside, the main shaft of the mill is the centre of a large circle formed by the sails, which consist of ninety-six double planks, placed perpendicularly. The wind rushing through the openings of these shutters acts with great power upon the sails, and, when it blows fresh, turns the mill with prodigious rapidity ; but this may be moderated in an instant by lessening the apertures between the shutters by the pulling of a rope. In this mill there are six pairs of stones." Captain Hooper's mill (later known as Fowler's mill) did not, however, survive very long, being found uneconomical in working.

Another oddly shaped mill takes us back to Lambeth, where existed at one time the Drug Mill of the Apothecaries' Company, used for grinding drugs and powders. It looked something like a tower-mill with a gallery and two little box-like erections on the top of the mill. Still on the Surrey side of the Thames, we could have found, in the last century, Freeman's Mill at Camberwell, a post-mill with tiled roundhouse and tail-pole, which formed a parochial boundary-mark ; not far away, on Dulwich Common, was Bree-Kill Mill, another post-mill dating from the eighteenth century. David Cox, who lived nearby in 1804, sketched this windmill, which was removed in 1870 when the present Dulwich College buildings were erected on the site.

The brickwork of a formerly attractive tower-mill remains at Plumstead, where it was built on to the Old Mill Inn. Vincent's *Records of the Woolwich District* mentions the following event : "The old mill on Plumstead Common was the scene of a startling occurrence in 1827. The mill was at that period in full work, and the housewives regularly carried their little store of wheat to the miller, Mr. Longmore (who also kept the 'Prince of Orange' in the village), to be ground into flour. A grand sham fight was arranged for the instruction of the neighbouring garrison, and the battle ranged from Bostall Heath to Woolwich. A number of Mr. Longmore's customers, friends and neighbours swarmed upon the staging round the mill, heedless of warning, until it gave way and injured several of them." Not many years afterwards this mill fell into disuse and "was diverted from the making of bread to the selling of beer."

At Islington a pair of windmills of the tower type were built two hundred years ago for working white lead ; the base of one remains, as does that of a mill at the premises of the Metropolitan Water Board in Rosebery Avenue. At Stratford three mills existed ; the last was wrecked by lightning about 1849, and previously some eight or ten mills were known to have been erected near the Isle of Dogs.

THE MILL AT CHESTERTON, WARWICKSHIRE
Nineteenth century engraving

The last working windmill in the capital may be found at Brixton, a five-storeyed tower-mill, built in 1816. The sails were removed as long ago as 1864, and after being out of commission for some time, work was recommenced by the use of a gas-engine, and still goes on. Probably best-known to Londoners is a mill which, while within the postal district of the metropolis, is under the authority of an out-county, in this case Surrey. Wimbledon Common Mill was built in 1817, a hollow post-mill, the only known example of its kind extant in Britain, and is mounted on a two-storey roundhouse. This windmill is no longer working but provides a favourite focal point for

BELOW LONDON BRIDGE
Detail from an etching by J. Nugent, 1821

walkers on the Common. The hollow post-mill derived its name from the fact that the machinery, which was all housed underneath the super-structure, was worked by a drive taken down from the sails through the hollow post.

We must move from London to see a windmill still at work under wind power, and if a visit is paid to the village of Terling, in Essex, we can find Mr. Herbert Bonner, the miller, busy on a windy day, although not so hard worked as he often has been since he started at Terling in 1900, after experience of a number of other mills.

His smock-mill, all white until 1929, and thus consuming much expensive paint, is now black and white, the body of the mill being tarred. Mr. Bonner, with his two assistants, used to paint the mill from top to bottom every three years, the application of two coats taking a month in good weather, working late. Mr. Bonner dresses his own stones, and remarks that there is always maintenance work to be done, sometimes at considerable cost. Recently the ninety-six cogs were stripped off his huge brake-wheel, 10 feet 7 inches in diameter, together with the fifty-seven on the spur-wheel, and these, with minor repairs to the sails, cost £75 to replace. Two of the present sails were bought some years ago off a disused mill at Diss, in Norfolk, taken by rail to the nearest station, and transported thence slung under two horse-drawn carts, for Mr. Bonner is always ingenious. The patent sails span sixty-six feet and are nine feet wide.

Clamber up the worn wooden stairs of Terling mill to the fourth floor, and then, if of an acrobatic disposition, you can follow the miller on to a further floor half-way up the cap and out for a breath of fresh air on to the staging of the fan-tail, which towers above. The sails go whirling by, one by one, and first of all, having returned to the fourth floor, Mr. Bonner will haul up sacks on the end of a long chain by means of the hoist, emptying the contents through trap-doors in the floor. Then down two storeys to the stones, of which there are three pairs, and an oat-crusher, where Mr. Bonner will keep his machinery at work, while belts, cog-wheels and stones move round in orderly and noisy profusion. A descent to the floor below will show the meal pouring out into sacks or bins. Mostly Mr. Bonner works by himself on animal foods, but there is not enough to keep him fully occupied, let alone his former employees. Only once in the last few years has the mill been the scene of stupendous activity, when a film company arrived to make scenes in a Will Hay comedy. It is tragic to see such a lovely mill not utilised to capacity.

The East Anglian counties are, perhaps more generally than any others, regarded as those containing windmills. A survey of Suffolk mills was published in 1941, and it was revealed that while in 1926 there were thirty-six post-mills working and two preserved, fifteen years later there were eight working, two preserved, twelve demolished and the remainder derelict. Of forty-eight smock- and tower-mills standing in 1926, including twenty-one working, by 1941 only three were at work, ten demolished and two preserved, the rest being derelict. A sorry tale indeed. In Norfolk there are nearly a hundred tower-mills, but only nine of these were working in 1940, when there were also the remains of a few post-mills and smock-mills which are here more uncommon. Many of the windmills on the Broads are, of course, used for draining and not for grinding at all, and Norfolk also possesses a number of watermills. This county's tower-mills are noted for their caps, shaped like an inverted rowing-boat. Elsewhere caps more or less peculiar to the locality are to be found ; in Lincolnshire,

A Miller in his Mill
Water colour by William Henry Hunt, c. 1815

for instance, the *ogee* type, shaped like the dome of an Eastern mosque, often with a ball surmounting the pinnacle. A common sort is a modified form of the latter, looking like an ordinary half-globe. Like chimney-pots, the size of caps is often deceptive ; it has been said, for instance, that more than twenty persons could comfortably stand underneath the cap of the smock-mill at West Chiltington in Sussex, which has now been converted into a house.

Conversion of tower-mills or smock-mills for residential purposes has a number of disadvantages; it is impossible to hang pictures properly on the sloping walls and patterned wallpaper would obviously never fit. Nevertheless, during this century a number of windmills have been turned into houses, some sympathetically, others in an unsightly manner. Naturally mills have been put to numerous other uses, perhaps the most degrading being one in Norfolk now used as a slaughter-house.

Lincolnshire, Cambridgeshire, Lancashire all contain many mills ; in Yorkshire there are only two post-mills and one of these, at Skirlaugh, with a high roundhouse giving a powerful appearance to the structure, was scheduled some time ago by the Office of Works as an ancient monument. On the islands of Anglesey and Holyhead there are a number of disused mills, one built in 1828 at Trearddur Bay being a most charming tower-mill until it was tail-winded in 1938 and the cap and sails torn off. Near Swansea there was a tower-mill at Kilvey Hill, but this once well-known landmark is now a heap of rubble. In the extreme west of Wales there worked until 1904, at St. David's, a tower-mill of great portliness, an enormous straight-sided construction resembling a treacle-tin. It was afterwards taken into the building of a hotel.

In Scotland, windmills have always been unusual, as is evidenced by Scott in *The Heart of Midlothian*, when Jeanie Deans writes from York: "All around the city are mills havena muckle wheels nor mill-dams, but gang by the wind—strange to behold !" One existed in the seventeenth century in the George Square district of Edinburgh, its purpose to raise water from the Burgh Loch to supply the brewers. It has long since disappeared. In 1704 the Earl of Hopetoun won a case before the Lords in Council concerning another windmill nearby at Leith. This mill was built to grind and refine ore from his lead-mines in Lanarkshire. It had fallen into disuse and the Earl employed one John Smith, who owned a sawmill at Leith, to repair it, incensing the wright-burgesses of Edinburgh, who could not do the work themselves, but were ready to interfere with anyone whom they regarded as violating their privileges.

A nineteenth-century water colour of Dublin, reproduced in Sean O'Faolain's *The Story of Ireland* in this Series, shows a windmill in the city, but Irish specimens are certainly rare. The last mill working by wind-power in Eire is at Tacumshin, County Wexford, where a fat white-washed tower-mill with a thatched roof is a conspicuous landmark.

DRAINING MILL, LINCOLNSHIRE

Water colour by John Sell Cotman, 1782 - 1842

CROWBOROUGH MILL, SUSSEX

Coloured line and wash drawing by Frank Brangwyn, 1923

ARTISTS WHO PAINTED MILLS

SAID Constable's brother, "when I look at a mill painted by John, I see that it will *go round*," and indeed we never find Constable depicting a windmill or watermill rendered impossible by unpracticality of construction or situation. Constable, like Rembrandt and Etty, was the son of a miller, and indeed spent his earlier years working in the trade. The beautiful and prosperous family watermill, which he made famous on canvas, was at Flatford, on the River Stour in Suffolk, and is now used as an art centre, besides being for a century a favourite subject for painters.

Constable was happiest in his native corner of England, and recorded the watermills at Dedham and East Bergholt, although there exist also his paintings of mills in Dorset and Sussex. In the latter county he sketched a number of windmills, but when travelling, he generally made a point of finding his way to "the *mill*, surrounded by weirs, backwaters, nets and willows, with a smell of weeds, flowing water and flour in my nostrils. . . . The sound of water escaping from mill-dams, etc., willows, old rotten planks, slimy posts and brickwork, I love such things." He kept his love to the end, for he was working on a picture of a mill on the last day of his life.

Constable's East Anglian contemporaries, John Crome and John Sell Cotman, also included windmills among their subjects. The two most celebrated of Crome's works, "Mousehold Heath" and "Moonrise on the Marshes of the Yare" both include windmills. Mousehold Heath is just outside Norwich, and Sprowston mill, generally reckoned to be the subject of Crome's picture, remained in excellent order until it was unfortunately destroyed by fire in 1933. In the Science Museum may be seen a cut-away model of this post-mill, to which a roundhouse was added in later years.

It is not generally known that Cotman made a drawing, now in the British Museum, which includes the same mill, and an etching exists by Crome himself in which Mousehold Heath was shown to boast not only the post-mill but a smock-mill as well.

Cotman, that masterly water-colourist, produced some of the most lovely windmill drawings in existence. Particularly may be mentioned his several sketches of Lincolnshire draining-mills. David Cox, who lived a large part of his life in the West, naturally painted watermills rather more, although he made many attractive studies of windmills. Examples of mills are also to be found in the work of Peter de Wint.

Among J. M. W. Turner's prolific works, especially his engravings, including the *Liber Studiorum*, may be found many depicting mills. Ruskin's comments on the subject entitled "Windmill and Lock" in the *Liber Studiorum*, are worth quoting, and he compares Turner's drawing with one by Clarkson Stanfield, another Royal Academician.

"I take, therefore, a windmill, forming the principal subject in his [Stanfield's] drawing of 'Brittany near Dol' [engraved in the *Coast Scenery*], and beside it I place a windmill, which forms also the principal subject in Turner's study of the Lock, in the *Liber Studiorum*. At first sight, I daresay, the reader may like Stanfield's best ; and there is indeed a great deal more in it to attract liking. Its roof is nearly as interesting as a piece of stony peak on a mountain, with a chalet built on its side ; and it is exquisitely varied in swell and curve. Turner's roof, on the contrary, is a plain ugly gable—a windmill roof and nothing more. Stanfield's sails are twisted into most effective wrecks, as beautiful as pine-bridges over Alpine streams ; only they do not look as if they had ever been serviceable wind-mill sails ; they are bent about in cross and awkward ways, as if they were warped or cramped, and their timbers look heavier than necessary. Turner's sails have no beauty about them, like that of Alpine-bridges ; but they have the exact switchy-sway of the sail that is always straining against the wind ; and the timbers form clearly the lightest possible framework for the canvas, thus showing the essence of windmill sail. Then the clay wall of Stanfield's mill is as beautiful as a piece of chalk cliff, all worn into furrows by the rain, coated with mosses, and rooted to the ground by a heap of crumbled stone, embroidered with grass and creeping plants. But this is not a service-able state for a windmill to be in. The essence of a windmill, as distinguished from all other mills, is, that it should turn round, and be a spinning thing, ready always to face the wind ; as light, therefore, as possible, and as vibratory ; so that it is in nowise good for it to approximate itself to the nature of chalk cliffs.

"Now observe how completely Turner has chosen his mill so as to mark this great fact of windmill nature ; how high he has set it ; how slenderly he has supported it ; how he has built it all of wood ; how he has bent the low planks so as to give the idea of the building lapping over the pivot on which it rests inside ; and how, finally, he has insisted on the great leverage of the beam behind it, while Stanfield's lever looks more like a prop than a thing to turn the roof with. And he has done all this fearlessly, though none of these elements of form are pleasant ones in themselves, but tend, on the whole, to give a somewhat mean and spider-like look to the principal feature in his picture, and then, finally, because he could not get the windmill dissected, and show us the real heart and centre of the whole, behold, he has put a pair of old millstones, lying outside, at the bottom of it. There—the first cause and motive of all the fabric—laid at its foundation ; and, beside them, the cart which is to fulfil the end of the fabric's being, and take home the sacks of flour. So far of what each painter chose to draw. But do not fail to consider the spirit in which it is drawn. Observe, that though all this ruin has befallen Stanfield's mill, Stanfield is not in the least sorry for it. On the contrary, he is delighted, and evi-dently thinks it is the most fortunate thing possible. The owner is ruined,

MARFORD MILL NEAR WREXHAM, DENBIGHSHIRE
Water colour by J. M. W. Turner, c. 1795

35

WINDMILL AND LOCK
Engraving from J. M. W. Turner's *Liber Studiorum*, 1807

doubtless, or dead, but his mill forms an admirable object in our view of Brittany . . . Not so, Turner. *His* mill is still serviceable ; but, for all that, he feels somewhat pensive about it."

Turner's watermills include one which scarcely grinds the miller's keep (*Liber Studiorum*, No. 37), a miserable sight altogether, yet Pembury Mill (No. 12) is entirely different, a happy, sturdy picture this upon which Stopford Brooke made the following comment : "The place is aware of itself and of the manifold human lives that have grown into it. There is, too, a special individuality which belongs to buildings which use water and wind for their work, and Turner has felt and seized that here. Therefore, with the old age there is quiet, and brightness, and distinction."

It is not until we come to the present century that we find another great painter particularly interested in windmills, and then in an entirely different style, for Sir Frank Brangwyn, R.A., found windmills not the charming, romantic subjects of a Cotman, but rugged material for his powerful brush. In Brangwyn's windmill pictures, many of which were published in book form in 1923, he captured, probably more than anyone else has ever done, the living individuality of the mills he depicted. English or Continental, working or wrecks, sunny or gaunt, his compositions amazingly catch the souls of each, and they are so alive that we might be standing there in front of the very structures he so vividly portrays.

THE WATERMILLS OF BRITAIN

WATERMILLS were introduced into this country in Anglo-Saxon times and the Domesday Survey records 7,500 of them. It is an undoubted fact that many mills still stand on exactly the same sites as they did nine hundred years ago, and it may even be that some of the actual buildings are of a like antiquity.

A considerable number of watermills were established by the abbots or priors of monasteries in order to cater for the large number of men connected with these establishments.

Through the mills, as also the bake-ovens, local tyranny was exerted by the abbots or the lords of the manor, for villeins were compelled to have their corn ground at the watermill, a system called thirlage, and to have their bread baked at the communal bake-ovens. The force of the law fell heavily upon anyone who attempted to evade these requirements by going elsewhere. A mill was sometimes rented to a miller, who might then be obliged to supply the stones for grinding. He obtained payment, or multure, by retaining part of the corn, and disputes frequently arose because of millers taking excessive amounts. A specimen multure is instanced as "a multur bowl from every two bushels of grain or of wheat, and a bowl from every bushel of unground grain."

The peasants would have been very pleased to have ground their corn by means of hand-mills at home, but this was not permitted. The Abbot of St. Albans paved his courtyard with stones taken from tenants. Such impositions were retained much longer in France and were a source of grievance even at the time of the French Revolution.

The Domesday Book details rents of mills, but owing to the vast difference between the currency of those days and our own, no useful comparison can be made. At Berlinge (Birling, Kent) the annual rental was 10s. and 330 eels, which were caught in the millstreams and eaten in great quantities at that time.

The advantage of both water and wind as prime movers is that they cost nothing, and that they are used but not consumed. It is not surprising that the water-wheel in its heyday was used to a very great extent for many industries, as up to fifty horse-power could easily be developed at much less cost than by any other method available at the time. It was simple to find places where suitable water power was ready, but it depended upon the height of the fall of water which type of wheel arrangement was installed. There are, broadly speaking, three types : overshot, breast and undershot installations. Where a sufficient fall of water obtains, it will be arranged to strike the wheel, usually through a chute, at its highest point, causing the buckets on the wheel to fill in turn and to rotate it forward by the weight of water. After about a third of a revolution the water is spilled out. The breast wheel has a similar principle, the difference being that the water strikes the wheel rather below its axis, causing it to turn against the current. The water is retained in the buckets for only one quarter of the revolution. The undershot installation is used when there is a much smaller fall of water, and it is the momentum which impels the wheel backwards in this case. Only a few of the buckets at the bottom can be filled, and the undershot wheel is reckoned to have only about half of the theoretical efficiency of the other types.

Watermills vary a great deal in floor space and height. The interior machinery is not greatly dissimilar from that of a windmill, and is usually arranged so that the axle of the water-wheel carries also a large toothed wheel, which engages with other cog-wheels on a vertical shaft, driving the millstones, a sack-hoist and other working parts. In 1938 the interior of Coldron Mill, from Spelsbury, Oxfordshire, was erected in the Science Museum, London. It is an eighteenth-century overshot construction, though a mill certainly existed on the site at the time of the Domesday Book. The sacks of grain were taken to the second floor by the hoist, and the grain poured through hoppers to the stones on the first floor, the flour being discharged by chutes into sacks on the lower floor.

In the *Millers', Merchants' and Farmers' Ready Reckoner*, published in 1861, can be found some interesting prices for milling equipment. A pair of "French burr stones, 5 feet diameter, bed stone flat, and the runner edge way of the burrs," cost £70, although less expensive stones could be obtained from other sources. A similar-sized pair of Peak stones, for instance, cost £30. Iron overshot water-wheels, each two feet wide, ranged in price from £340 for twenty feet diameter to £530 for thirty-two feet diameter, and it can easily be seen from these and other prices quoted that the establishment of a new watermill was no inexpensive matter in those days. The same book gives tables for the revolution of the wheel in ratio to the height of the fall of water. If the fall is one foot the wheel will turn 2.83 times per minute, but if the fall is twenty feet it will turn 12.68 times.

Besides the grinding of grain, or of the many other kinds of food such as cattle-food to which some of these old mills have been reduced, it must be remembered that at one time the water-wheel provided the motive-power for industries of all kinds. Smeaton alone erected forty-three watermills, nearly all for industrial use. Paper mills at one time used water-wheels, as did woollen and cotton mills. Before the coming of steam-power Derbyshire and not Lancashire was the great cotton county, the deep valleys with rushing streams from the Pennines proving very suitable for the siting of the imposing mill buildings. The pioneer Arkwright built his first mill near Matlock in 1771. In Wales, where the woollen industry has been long established, small factory units still exist, especially in the Tywi and Teifi valleys, utilising water-power and hand-looms. Cloth fulling mills are known to the Welsh as "pandy" mills, which has influenced many place-names in that country. The Weald of Surrey and Sussex was formerly

WATERMILL
Illumination from the Luttrell Psalter, *c.* 1340

the great iron-producing district, and water-power was used to operate the bellows of the blast-furnaces. The revolving wheel caused the cams on the shaft to press down the bellows, which were raised again by counter-weights on the beam overhead. Where insufficient water-power was available, hammerponds were constructed, and became a feature of the locality; but owing to the discovery of a method of coal smelting, the whole industry moved to the north, and in 1820 the last Wealden charcoal furnace closed.

Two industries which were formerly carried on in Yorkshire were flint and cement grinding. At Sprotborough Mill flint was ground to a fine powder and shipped to Spain for the making of china. At Sandsend, Mulgrave cement was made for three generations; it had an unrivalled reputation for quick setting, making it especially valuable for work in water. The cement stones were burned in a kiln, and then reduced by one set of millstones to the size of a split-pea, and by another set to a powder. Both of these mills at one time ground corn, and we frequently find to-day that a watermill still working is busy grinding all kinds of things. Another Yorkshire mill, which is in daily operation, can be found at Welton, near Hull. It is more than a century old and still in excellent condition. The present wheel was installed in 1861, is thirty-six feet in diameter, and has 128 buckets, each of which holds about ten gallons of water. The wheel weighs nearly ten tons. A short way off is the mill-dam, whence the water is conducted by a culvert to the wheel itself, a slide mechanism controlling the amount of water required at this point, as for light work the full water-power is not needed. Surplus water is drained away.

Sizes of wheels vary a great deal and some are very much broader than others. One of the most famous mills in the south of England, at

Mapledurham, Oxfordshire, has a larger than usual breadth of wheel. This mellow-tiled mill has existed since Saxon times and about twelve sacks of corn are still ground weekly for local use, although the mill is busier in the winter. The millstones each weigh a ton and are fourteen feet in circumference. They are expected to have a life of fifty years. At this mill may be seen flood marks cut on the door by the various millers; in 1768 the mill was flooded to a depth of four feet. It is not uncommon for mills to be flooded and this is by no means the only example which bears such flood marks. It was drought more than flood which the old miller feared, however, and he had to deal with his vagaries of power-supply in a very similar way to the miller who depended on the wind.

The decline of the watermill may be said to have set in rather earlier than the decline of the windmill, for while the latter was principally used for grinding corn, the watermill, as we have seen, at one time provided a great motive-force in industry, although at all times it had its share in the grinding of grain, and retained this work with the windmill for some while after it had lost its importance in the general industrial field. Competition from more reliable and powerful motive-forces, such as the steam-engine, very quickly caused the water-wheel to be supplanted. There was a limit to the capacity of the wheel, the diameter of which should not be less than the height of the fall of water, from which it will be obvious that as constructional difficulties would present themselves in making wheels greatly larger than the usual size, a wheel of no type, whether overshot, breast or undershot, would be able to develop the power of a very considerable water-force. During the expansion of manufacture following the Industrial Revolution, it was to the obvious advantage of industrialists to seize the opportunities presented by new methods of motive-power. The rapid growth of the towns where labour was readily available guided the siting of factories, and the building of railways also tended to militate against the continued use of water-powered mills, inaccessibly situated as they usually were. Thus it came about that watermills remained in being only as corn-mills until they were also largely ousted from this work by the roller mills, except in the remoter parts of the land. Progress has taken us to the point where we can scarcely meet a miller or any other working tradesman, and nowadays instead of seeing the miller about his work, with the wheel and stones busily turning, we must view the millhouse neglected and uninhabited, the stream chattering away as it has done for years, but the wheel idle if not broken quite, and fortunate indeed to have escaped the attention of the iron-hunters of two wars. It would not cost a veteran miller £530 to replace his wheel to-day; he could doubtless obtain a good one for scrap price.

As has been noted, a few counties have possessed a considerable number of both watermills and windmills, but it is more usual to find that they are situated in separate areas of Great Britain. Kent, Surrey and Norfolk

MILL BRIDGE AND WATERFALL

Water colour by Andrew Hunt, 1790 - 1861

WATERMILL

are three counties in which both abounded. Two Kentish water-mills quite close to London and to each other are at Bexley and Farningham. Both are weatherboarded and painted white ; the former busily working still, and the latter a perfect gem, set back from the road, and fronted by a large closely-cropped lawn, bounded by old stone cottages. Familiar to many is another mill situated on a powerful river but with the wheel now rusty and disused : the Castle Mill, Dorking, Surrey, a county which retains a moderate number of watermills. The one at Milton Court has been most cruelly treated, part of the mill buildings having been demolished and the remains of the giant overshot wheel scattered around to lie rotting, a very different sight from when it was in production during last century.

The Wandle, another Surrey river, which rises on the North Downs, and joins the Thames in the London suburbs at Wandsworth, falls 124 feet in nine miles, and in consequence of the uncommon power thus developed and its nearness to the capital, was always greatly utilised for industry, and was once described as the hardest-worked river of its size in the world. It has a long history of watermills, which may even stretch back to Roman times, for the water-wheel, *mola aquaria*, was known to the Romans, and described by Strabo and Vitruvius. Certain it is that the Domesday Survey recorded thirteen on the Wandle, which grew by 1610 to twenty-four. At that date, it was proposed to divert some of the water of the Wandle, and vigorous opposition being made by the millers and local inhabitants, a Royal Commission was set up which pronounced against the scheme. The evidence held that the population of Surrey and London "cannot be so conveniently served with meale at any tyme, as by the said milles, and especially in the tyme of the greate froste this river never freezeth." Moreover, it was claimed, the King would suffer, "in respect of his milles, which are in number sixe, and of the best seated in the said river." The number and size of industries on the Wandle, apart from flour-milling, make it a river of especial interest. Here was set up a mill for the fulling of cloth, as early as 1376 ; close by was a mill grinding pigments for colouring pottery, and others for bleaching, while during the course of the eighteenth century calico-printing became the predominant industry. In 1805 a census was taken which showed on the Wandle twelve mills engaged on calico-printing, nine flour-mills, five snuff-mills, three bleaching-mills, three oil-mills, two dyeing-mills, one each paper-mill, skinning-mill, logwood-mill (used in dyeing), copper-mill, iron works and porter brewery. The importance of the Wandle industries began to decline about 1850, but the most famous of them was yet to come, for it was on the Wandle at Merton Abbey that William Morris established his new works in 1881, in mellowed premises that had been erected for silk-weaving in the previous century. Morris, of course, was not content with one product, and there would be the bustle of contented and varied activity within the wooden walls, while outside the Wandle worked the water-wheel amid gardens that

LAKENHAM MILLS, NORWICH, NORFOLK
Water colour by John Sell Cotman, 1782-1842

would be filled with flowers in the summer-time, companioned by the equally gay chintzes or yarn rinsing or drying nearby.

In London, watermills existed until fairly recently at Tottenham and Catford, where three were demolished about 1912. Turnmill Street, Clerkenwell, commemorates a brook associated with the River Fleet, and as early as the reign of Henry IV it was known under the similar name of Trylmyl Streate. Several mills existed here, and we find in the *Daily Courant* in 1741 an advertisement of a house in Bowling Alley, off Turnmill Street, with a good stream and current, "that will turn a mill to grind hair-powder or liquorish, and other things."

A trip along the upper reaches of the Thames would yield a considerable number of watermills ; one does not go very far in either direction from Henley, for instance, before encountering a large mill, one of these, Hambleden, being a most pleasant white weatherboarded specimen, and the most striking mill anywhere on the Thames. It is not without significance that at nearly every lock between Oxford and Marlow a watermill has existed ; Mapledurham has already been mentioned, and Iffley Mill, backed by the square Norman church tower, was familiar to every Oxford University

IFFLEY MILL, NEAR OXFORD
Water colour by Alfred Rimmer, 1829-1893

43

man, and the subject of many pictures by brush and camera until it was unfortunately destroyed by fire in 1908. The first mill on the stripling Thames is at Somerford Keynes.

Berkshire is surprisingly rich in watermills, of the undershot type. The Abbey mill at Abingdon, a town beloved by Ruskin, has two wheels, one much broader than the other. Neither of these is visible from the outside, as they are situated within and beneath the mill. This explains why in many watermills the undershot wheel cannot be seen except from the interior, the brick arches over the tail-race and outlet being the only evidence to the casual observer of the function of the building. This mill is now mainly used as a store, although a little animal food is still ground occasionally. It is the miller's custom to turn the large green-elm wheel for a spell daily to keep it from rotting, and then it can be seen in the mill from a stage over the stream, turning rapidly backwards, and shot by streaks of light as the dripping floats rotate. The other wheel is in need of repair. The white-washed interior of the mill is cool on a hot summer's day, and the prevailing impression is of orderliness amid much tackle and sacks and timber. Except when the mill is at work, the green water is checked before it reaches the wheels, and rushes beneath away from them with an insistent pounding; when the wheel is turned merely to keep it in condition, the stones are left stationary and impotent; a blue dragonfly or two may sleep on a window-pane, and cobwebs lie all around, and the mill is quiet compared with yesteryear.

It is in the west country, and in Wales particularly, that we can discover numerous overshot watermills, as the mountainous nature of some of the countryside develops much water-power. One of the most interesting mills in this locality is the big Abbey Mill at Tewkesbury, the original of Abel Fletcher's mill in Mrs. Craik's *John Halifax, Gentleman*, and thought by some to be also the inspiration of *The Mill on the Floss* by George Eliot. It was recently acquired by the town council, who are to preserve it.

A notorious highwayman, Thomas Boulter, made Poulshot Mill, Wiltshire, his headquarters for several years two centuries ago. Smugglers, too, had reputed associations with both watermills and windmills. A few years ago an ingenious hiding-place for contraband goods was discovered at Coolham, Sussex, where nearly seventy wine bottles—empty, alas!—were found during repairs in a cavity hidden by a large stone beneath the sluice of an undershot wheel.

A Hampshire mill of exceptional interest is the Chesapeake Mill at Wickham, constructed from the wood of the American frigate *Chesapeake*, captured off Boston by Rear-Admiral Philip Broke of the English *Shannon* in 1813 after a memorable duel. The *Chesapeake* was brought back to England and became a unit of the British Navy until she was broken up in 1820, and her timbers incorporated in the watermill, which survived to do useful work for more than a century afterwards.

WATERMILL AT GRESS IN THE HEBRIDES
Water colour by Charles Skilton, 1945

In Scotland watermills abound, and were used for tweed-making among other things. To anyone interested in watermill hunting, the lure of tracing a mill may turn out an exacting if exciting experience, leading to very strange places, and to the present writer the most fascinating memories are recalled of visits to the Western Isles. Here, on the sunny days, may be found colours surely unequalled in Britain, while the general atmosphere and the character of the local people strike a very refreshing note. On Lewis there are watermills at Garrabost, still working but with a gas-engine as the water current dried up, and at Gress, a tiny hamlet near Tolsta. Here the writer had the odd experience of alighting by chance from a long motor-bus excursion and finding the mill there by accident— or was it instinct ?—afterwards meeting the woman who was miller until operations ceased in 1940. Several examples have existed on Mull, and a solidly-built specimen was discovered at Ardfeinig, temporarily out of action. Here the miller, a strong and handsome old man, was busily shearing sheep when the writer called, but took time off for a conducted tour of the mill, which was erected about sixty years ago by order of the 8th Duke of Argyll, and brought from Cumnock, Ayrshire. The wheel has a circumference of 52 feet, and the mill can grind 120 bushels of corn per hour.

David I in the charter of the foundation of Holyrood, granted to the monks "one of my mills of Dene, a tithe of the mill of Liberton and of Dene, and of the new mill of Edinburgh," 1143-47. King David also founded Canonmills, a district still thus named, and in 1682 Alexander Hunter, lessee of the Canonmills, was prosecuted by Peter de Bruis, whose paper-mill, newly erected nearby for the monopoly manufacture of playing-cards, Hunter had pulled down. Hunter counter-claimed on account of the throwing of his wife into the mill-race, for which exploit de Bruis was fined £50. Another spectacle of immersion in water, this time voluntary, could be seen about 1652 when Anabaptists took the plunge. Says Nicoll in his diary : "Thrice weekly, namely, on Monday, Wednesday and Friday, there were dippit at Bonnington Mill, betwixt Leith and Edinburgh, both men and women of good rank." Evidences of mills at Bonnington, where the water-wheel was discarded in the early years of this century, and around Bell's Mills, near Dean Bridge, where the road leaves Edinburgh for Queensferry, are still obvious. All the mills named are on Edinburgh's little river, the Water of Leith.

In some places can be discovered mills worked by the tide, and not by a running stream. In London, two semi-tidal mills exist still at Bromley-by-Bow, with a history going back to the twelfth century. One of these mills, which are used for grinding barley and other grain for a distillery, has four wheels and the other three, each developing from twenty to forty-five horse-power.

An investigation into existing tidal-mills led to the announcement by Rex Wailes, an authority on mills, that twenty-three examples remained in 1938, of which ten were still working by the original motive-power. The one at Woodbridge, Suffolk, has a wooden wheel, twenty feet in diameter, and nearly six feet wide, the oak shaft being twenty-two inches square. Others still at work were at Emsworth, Sussex, Beaulieu and Eling in Hampshire, Stambridge, Essex, and in Wales at Carew and Pembroke. William Catt, owner of a tidal-mill at Bishopstone, Sussex, a century and a half ago, made a fortune of nearly half a million pounds from his mill, which was erected in 1761 by Act of Parliament. In 1834 it was said to have run sixteen pairs of stones, although four were originally installed. Another very charming structure of the same kind, Birdham Mill, may be seen near Chichester, although it was recently converted into a yacht repair shop.

Of Beaulieu Mill, H. J. Massingham wrote : "Part of the mill is built out on piles into the river and is weatherboarded, while the rest of the building is a warm red brick roofed with lozenge-shaped and rounded tiles, which I believe are called fish-tiles. All the interior is of wood—ladders, bins for the meal, floor-boarding, square pillars, beams, narrow passages, fittings, shaft rising to the first floor and all. So ramshackle is the arrangement of the props and supports that it is a wonder why the whole edifice does not tumble about the miller's ears like a pack of cards. The point is that it has stood in this very way for something like six centuries, and that gives the explorer into its dusky depths a more penetrating notion of how the old builders could build, more than does a Gothic church or even a cathedral. The pulse and swing of the great wheel sets the whole building in an ague, but it will be still standing when all the flimsy excrescences of development between Beaulieu and Poole have fallen down."

It seems incredible that Beaulieu is just a relic from the 27,000 water-mills once in active production, operated by craftsmen who knew the joys of creative labour. The age when such work was appreciated seems past; by the unpleasant products of modern factories the people are now fed; in the slick, mechanised world of to-day many of the beauties of life have been lost. To regain our heritage, as Mr. Massingham says in *Where Man Belongs*, "it needs a wiser civilisation than ours, a civilisation that puts value first and profits second." The few watermills and windmills still in daily use serve to remind us of a more genuine way of life to which we should return.

TIDAL-MILL, WOODBRIDGE, SUFFOLK
Drawing by W. P. Robins, 1940

47

SHORT BIBLIOGRAPHY

History of Corn Milling by Richard Bennett and John Elton. 4 vols. 1898-1904, Simpkin, Marshall.—*Windmills* by Frank Brangwyn and Hayter Preston. 1923, John Lane.—*Old Watermills and Windmills* by R. Thurston Hopkins. 1930, P. Allan & Co., London.—*English Windmills* : Vol. I (Kent, Surrey, Sussex) by M. I. Batten ; Vol. II (Essex, Hertfordshire, Buckinghamshire, Middlesex, London) by Donald Smith ; 1930, 1932, Architectural Press, London.—*England of the Windmills* by S. P. B. Mais. 1931, Dent.—*Windmill Land* by C. Allen Clarke. 2nd ed., 1933, W. Foulsham & Co., London.—*Watermills and Windmills* by William Coles Finch. 1933, C. W. Daniel Co., London.—*Windmills in Sussex* by Rev. Peter Hemming. 1936, C. W. Daniel Co., London